GRAPHIC EXPEDITIONS

THE MESA VERDE
CLIFF DWELLERS

AN *Isabel Soto*
HISTORY ADVENTURE

Terry Collins

illustrated by Cynthia Martin and Barbara Schulz

Raintree

R www.raintreepublishers.co.uk
Visit our website to find out
more information about
Raintree books.

To order:
☎ Phone 0845 6044371
🖺 Fax +44 (0) 1865 312263
🖾 Email myorders@raintreepublishers.co.uk

Customers from outside the UK please telephone +44 1865 312262

Raintree is an imprint of Capstone Global Library Limited, a company incorporated in England and
Wales having its registered office at 7 Pilgrim Street, London EC4V 6LB
Registered company number: 6695882

Text © Capstone Press 2010
First published by Capstone Press in 2010
First published in hardback in the United Kingdom by Capstone Global Library Ltd in 2011
The moral rights of the proprietor have been asserted.

British Library Cataloguing in Publication Data
Collins, Terry – The Mesa Verde Cliff Dwellers: an Isabel Soto history investigation
A full catalogue record for this book is available from the British Library.

ISBN 978 1 406 22590 7 (hardback)
15 14 13 12 11
10 9 8 7 6 5 4 3 2 1

Designer: Alison Thiele
Cover artist: Tod Smith
Colourist: Michael Kelleher
Media researcher: Wanda Winch
Editors: Aaron Sautter and Diyan Leake
Originated by Capstone Global Library Ltd
Printed and bound in China by South China Printing Company Limited

Disclaimer
All the Internet addresses (URLs) given in this book were valid at the time of going to press.
However, due to the dynamic nature of the Internet, some addresses may have changed, or sites may
have changed or ceased to exist since publication. While the publisher regrets any inconvenience this
may cause readers, no responsibility for any such changes can be accepted by the publisher.

...therill Family, 9; Library of Congress, 17; U.S.
...l Parks Service/Mesa Verde National Park, 23

...en Ping Hung (framed edge design); mmmm (world
...tract lines design); Najin (old parchment design)

CONTENTS

On 18 December 1888, Richard Wetherill and Charles Mason were caught in a snowstorm while looking for lost cattle. But they found a lost city instead.

What's that?

It looks like a city built right into the cliff!

The two men found handholds carved into the sandstone. They decided to climb down for a closer look.

No, not a city. More like a palace — a palace of stone.

Be careful! These rocks are slippery!

Cowboy explorer

Richard Wetherill (1858–1910) was a rancher who was fascinated with the sites left behind by the ancient Pueblo people. He gladly served as a guide for visitors to Cliff Palace. Although he loved the dwellings, he and others caused some unintended damage while searching for artefacts to add to their collections.

Some researchers think the cliff dwellers came to Mesa Verde because the top of the mesa had good land for farming.

Others believe the village was built within the cliff face to escape bad weather on the open mesa above.

The cliff dwellings would be cooler in the summer and warmer in the winter.

Some experts think the cliff dwellers came here to escape attacks from enemy tribes.

They weren't looking for a fight, but they would defend their homes if they were attacked.

The ancient Pueblo were a peaceful people. Their days were spent building additions to the village, hunting, drying hides, and preparing food.

The ancient Pueblo left these dwellings more than 700 years ago. We aren't sure why they left. There may be several reasons.

Which is why I asked you to come, Izzy. Let's keep moving. I want to show you a few things.

Thanks for the tour, Ranger Smith.

Amazing! The stones fit together so closely.

The round tower is one of the most recognizable parts of Cliff Palace.

The room inside is perfectly round too. Let's take a look.

The ancient Pueblo may have used this tower to watch for invaders.

That makes sense.

You can easily see down into the canyon through these peepholes.

That's right. But the roofs were very sturdy when built.

The open area on top of the roof was even used as a courtyard. Adults could gather there to prepare food or make crafts. And children would play near their parents.

A hole was left in the centre of the kiva's roof. It allowed smoke to escape from the room below.

The hole was also the kiva's main entrance. People used a wooden ladder to enter and leave the kiva.

This small hole near the floor is interesting. What is it?

This opening is part of an airshaft that leads to the kiva's roof. It allowed fresh air to enter and push smoke from the fire out through the roof.

Dr Goode, here's the artefact you wanted.

Hold on, we'll be right up.

We recently found this Mesa Verde mug. It's in perfect condition.

I've seen ancient pottery before. But this mug doesn't look very old.

PRESERVING THE PAST

After the cliff dwelling sites were discovered, people from all over the world began to explore Mesa Verde. They stole many rare artefacts. Other people damaged and vandalized the sites. The US government agreed to help protect the dwellings. On 29 June 1906, President Theodore Roosevelt made Mesa Verde a national park.

Mesa Verde mugs look very modern. But they are hundreds of years old.

We've found a lot of pottery here at Cliff Palace. Most items are simple plates, bowls, or jars.

However, we occasionally find a special mug. Try shaking this one next to your ear.

RATTLE
RATTLE

Is something broken inside?

Not at all. This "shaker" mug has a false bottom. Several clay pellets were hidden inside when the mug was made.

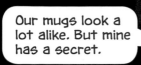

RATTLE
RATTLE

RATTLE
RATTLE

21

DENTAL PROBLEMS

Ancient Pueblo women used a handheld stone called a mano to grind corn for meals. They crushed the kernels of corn against a flat stone slab called a metate. Grit from the stones mixed in with the cornmeal. Over time, the grit in their food wore down the Pueblos' teeth.

25

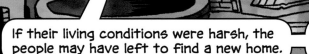

No rain meant a shortage of food. And it may have led to conflicts with their neighbours.

If their living conditions were harsh, the people may have left to find a new home.

Unfortunately, we may never know for certain why they left.

The ancient Pueblo people may be gone. But as long as Cliff Palace is here, we can continue to learn about the people who once lived here long ago.

MORE ABOUT
MESA VERDE

The ancient Pueblo people were once known by the Navajo word *anasazi*. *Anasazi* can mean various things such as "other ancestors" or "ancient ones not like us". This name is not used today. Researchers believe the cliff dwellers had no specific name at all. They simply called themselves "the people".

Today, many Pueblo people still enter the cliff dwellings to pray. They believe the spirits of their ancestors inhabit the ancient villages that are found throughout Mesa Verde.

The ancient Pueblo people had a very short life span. Most lived 32 to 34 years. However, some lived into their 50s and 60s. About half of all children died before the age of 5 due to disease.

While some researchers think the round tower was used to watch for enemies, others think it may have had a different use. The ancient Pueblo were known to be "sky watchers". They watched the patterns of the sky to determine the seasons. The tower may have been used to watch the sky, rather than as a lookout spot.

The walls of Cliff Palace are made of sandstone blocks held together by mud mortar. The ancient Pueblo chipped out and shaped the blocks with stone axes. They then applied a thin layer of mud to make the walls smooth.

The ancient Pueblo people grew corn, beans, and squash for food. They also hunted deer and rabbits for meat. They gathered wild plants, roots, berries, nuts, seeds, and fruits. Some researchers think the Pueblo people even ate the stems of the prickly pear cactus.

 The ancient Pueblo also raised turkeys just as farmers raise chickens today. They ate both the turkeys and their eggs. They used the turkeys' feathers to make warm blankets and robes.

MORE ABOUT

NAME: Isabel "Izzy" Soto
INTERESTS: People and places
BUILD: Athletic   **HAIR:** Dark brown
EYES: Brown   **HEIGHT:** 1.70 m

WISP: The Worldwide Inter-dimensional Space/Time Portal developed by Max Axiom at Axiom Laboratory.

BACKSTORY: Isabel "Izzy" Soto caught the humanities bug as a little girl. Every night, her grandfather told her about his adventures exploring ancient ruins in South America. He believed people can learn a lot from other cultures and places.

Izzy's interest in cultures followed her through school and beyond. She studied history and geography. On one research trip, she discovered an ancient stone with mysterious energy. Izzy took the stone to Super Scientist Max Axiom, who determined that the stone's energy cuts across space and time. Harnessing the power of the stone, he built a device called the WISP. It opens windows to any place and any time. Although she must not use the WISP to change history, Izzy now explores events wherever and whenever they happen, solving a few mysteries along the way.

GLOSSARY

artefact object made and used by people in the past

cliff dwelling room or building built under an overhanging cliff for protection from the weather

courtyard open area surrounded by walls

drought long spell of very dry weather

kiva underground chamber used mainly for religious ceremonies

mano handheld stone used for grinding corn into cornmeal

mesa hill or mountain with steep sides and a flat top

metate stone block with a shallow indentation used for grinding corn and other grains

mortar a mixture of lime, sand, water, and cement that is used for building

restore bring back to an original condition

sandstone a kind of rock made up of sandlike grains of quartz cemented together by lime or other materials

vandalize needlessly damage or destroy somebody else's property

FIND OUT MORE

Books

Mesa Verde (Excavating the Past), Mary Quigley (Heinemann Library, 2006)

Mesa Verde (Visiting the Past), Jane Shuter (Heinemann Library, 2001)

Mesa Verde National Park (Symbols of Freedom: National Parks), Nancy Dickmann (Heinemann Library, 2006)

Internet sites

www.mesaverde.com/Slideshows/mesaverde/mvslide01.htm
Visit this website to see slideshow of pictures of the buildings at Mesa Verde, as well as some beautiful pottery.

www.ourplaceworldheritage.com
Enter "Mesa Verde" into the search field on this World Heritage website to learn more and see photos of the Mesa Verde buildings.